TRINITY GUILDHALL

Sound at Sight

Piano

book 3

Grades 6-8

Published by
Trinity College London
89 Albert Embankment
London SE1 7TP UK

T +44 (0)20 7820 6100
F +44 (0)20 7820 6161
E music@trinityguildhall.co.uk
www.trinityguildhall.co.uk

Printed in England by Halstan & Co. Ltd, Amersham, Bucks.

Sound at sight

Playing or singing music that has not been seen before is a necessary part of any musician's life, and the exploration of a new piece should be an enjoyable and stimulating process.

Reading music requires two main components: firstly, the ability to grasp the meaning of music notation on the page; secondly, the ability to convert sight into sound and perform the piece. This involves imagining the sound of the music before playing it. This in turn implies familiarity with intervals, chord shapes, rhythmic patterns and textures. The material in this series will help pianists to develop their skills and build confidence.

Plenty of pieces are given throughout, but this is more than just a book of specimen tests. Guidance is given on new skills before they are incorporated in short pieces of music. This contributes to making this a thoroughly practical course in developing sight reading skills, whether it is used for examination preparation or to increase confidence in the context of solo playing or ensemble work.

Trinity Guildhall's sight reading requirements are stepped progressively between Initial and Grade 8, with manageable increases in difficulty between each grade. Some tips on examination preparation are given at the back of the book. In all cases, however, references to examination tests are avoided until *after* the relevant material has been practised. This is deliberate: many pupils find the prospect of being tested on sight reading skills to be quite inhibiting at first. The aim is to perform new pieces – the fact that they may be examination tests as well is far less important.

Acknowledgements

Thanks are due to the many composers who have contributed to the series: James Burden, Humphrey Clucas, Colin Cowles, David Dawson, Sébastien Dédis, Peter Fribbins, David Gaukroger, Robin Hagues, Amy Harris, Peter Lawson, Jonathan Paxman, Danielle Perrett and Michael Zev Gordon.

Thanks are also due to Matthew Booth, Luise Horrocks, Geraint John, Joanna Leslie and Anne Smillie for their technical advice.

The *udjat* symbol is an Egyptian hieroglyph called the 'sound eye', and was associated with the god Horus.

● Introduction

If you have worked through books 1 and 2 in this series, you will already be quite experienced in sight reading.

Many of the necessary skills will already have been mastered. The most useful of these skills is the ability to look ahead and choose a fingering which will work and enable you to reach the next note, and to play it how you want to, without having to look down. If you do need to look down, you risk losing your place on the page and therefore interrupting the flow of the music.

At this level, pieces will demand a increasing degree of musical understanding and awareness of style. Appropriate techniques need to be employed to create the effect that the music requires. Part of the skill of the sight reader, therefore, is to judge the effect that is required and to match it with the appropriate technique.

It is essential that you start with a good foundation in aural training. Make sure that you are thoroughly at home with recognising chords and textures.

Another thing to look for in pieces at this level is modulation. Try to notice if the modulation is going to a sharper/higher key (dominant, relative major, supertonic etc) or a flatter/lower one (subdominant, relative minor etc.). Try to anticipate the sound of the new tonic in your head each time the music changes key.

• Balance, phrasing and pedalling

Be ready to balance the parts at any time. This involves playing the important part louder than the supporting accompaniment, whichever hand it is in. Repeated chords must be played quietly to avoid them dominating the sound (as in no. 1 here).

You should also aim to phrase sensibly: getting louder as the notes rise and getting quieter as they fall will make a difference in itself.

The sustaining pedal will be required in many pieces now, although it may not be specifically marked. Change pedal frequently, as the harmonies require, or use the pedal only some of the time to enhance the colour of the sound. Do not allow 'wall-to-wall' pedalling to smother a lively or delicate piece.

8 Moderato

9 Piangevole e con rubato

10 Moderato

11 Deciso

12 Con moto

13 Moderato

14 **Tempo comodo**

15 **Gently**

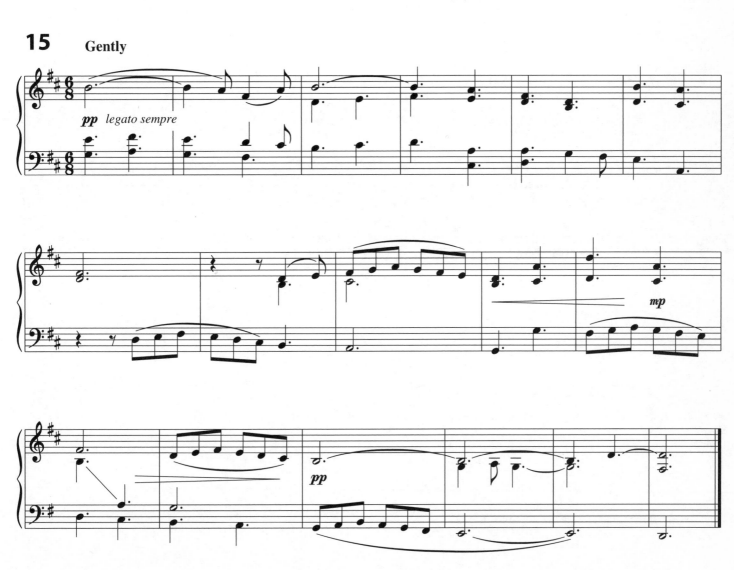

16 Vivace

 Melodies 1-16 are of the standard used by Trinity Guildhall for Grade 6 examinations.

• Colour and style

As the length increases, there should be increased understanding of the whole shape of the piece and how smaller phrases build to make the larger shape. This can be achieved by increasing the volume of each little phrase until the climax then decreasing to the end. This planning can be built into your preparation time before playing the piece through.

Recognising and reproducing an appropriate style is necessary here. Use a different touch for Baroque, Classical, Romantic or Impressionistic styles. Contemporary styles are also increasingly likely.

An important difference between this level and previous ones is that the pedal will need more imaginative use to add colour to the music. Watch out for isolated bass notes that must remain sounding during wandering accompaniments, for example.

There will also be more occasions where you encounter chromaticism. Use your aural sense to spot intervals between the notes of the melody and chord shapes with which you may be familiar from playing in another key. Do not forget that an accidental applies throughout the bar: this is obvious but can easily be overlooked when reading a piece for the first time.

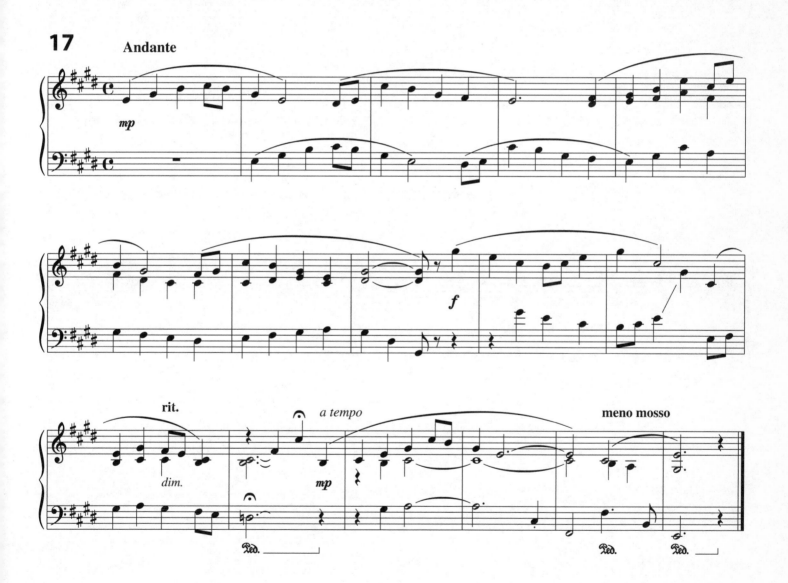

18

Andantino

19

20

21 **Gracefully**

22 Tempo di valse

23 Chaconne (lento)

24

25 **Maestoso**

 Melodies 17–25 are of the standard used by Trinity Guildhall for Grade 7 examinations.

• Increasing variety

As pieces have more and more notes, you need to remember to vary the volume in moving lines. It is easy to think because you are playing faster that the music is alive but these faster notes need direction at all times, in both hands, in both short and long phrases.

Keys now include the widest possible range. Make sure that you are familiar with rarely encountered keys such as G# minor. Select fingerings carefully to ensure that you can play the next note or notes purely by feel. Many silent changes will be needed as well as constant use of everyday scale and arpeggio fingerings. A free arm will be of enormous help if all this is to happen effortlessly.

Some of the pieces here are in obviously familiar styles (Bach, Haydn and Shostakovich are all represented, amongst others). Make sure that the style of playing reflects this, with the right touch (hand or arm weight), appropriate articulation and pedalling.

Chromaticism is central to many pieces at this stage. Be sure to observe the key that you are moving into or through. Notes that are dissonant to the harmony should usually receive more stress than those that are part of the chord, so a good aural sense is very important in enabling you to identify such moments.

27 **Playfully**

28 Allegretto

29

30 **Decisive**

31

Con moto

32 Poco adagio

33　Tempo di valse

34 Quasi gavotta

35 Allegro ritmico

36

 Melodies 26-36 are of the standard used by Trinity Guildhall for Grade 8 examinations.

• Examination preparation

In an examination, you have half a minute to prepare your performance of the sight reading test.

It is important to use this time wisely. You will immediately notice the key and time signature. Check whether the key is major or minor. Try to grasp the style of the piece quickly too—its rhythmic character and pace. Does the texture remind you of a style you have played in before? Look for the climax point (the loudest moment) and observe the other dynamics in order to plan your shaping of the piece.

Set the pace securely in your head and read through the test, imagining the sound under your fingers. It might help to tap any awkward rhythms in the music or to try out some of it but the most important thing is to get a clear idea of what the music will sound like.

Have you imagined the effect of the pedal?

When the examiner asks you to play the piece, play it at the pace you have set. The rhythm is more important than anything else: keep going at all costs! If you make a little slip, do not try to go back and change it – the mistake has already gone. Make sure instead that the next thing is right.

Give a performance of the piece. If you can play the pieces in this book, you will be well prepared for examination sight reading, so enjoy the opportunity to play another piece that you did not know before.